Clifford THE BIG RED DOG

THE PUMPKIN PIE PRIZE

by Acton Figueroa
Illustrated by John Kurtz

Based on the Scholastic book series
"Clifford The Big Red Dog"
by Norman Bridwell

Designed by Michael Massen

ISBN 0-439-75532-8

10 9 8 7 6 5 4 3 2 1   05 06 07 08 09
Printed in the U.S.A.
First Printing, October 2005

SCHOLASTIC INC.

New York   Toronto   London   Auckland   Sydney
Mexico City   New Delhi   Hong Kong   Buenos Aires

On a sunny fall Saturday, Emily Elizabeth and Clifford walked to the park.

They were going to the Birdwell Island
Harvest Day Festival.

Emily Elizabeth was very excited.

"Look, Clifford!" said Emily Elizabeth.

"The biggest pumpkin contest has started!"

Farmers had brought giant pumpkins.

Principal Rodriguez was the judge.

Emily Elizabeth and Clifford were amazed

at how big pumpkins can grow!

"What are your plans for today?" asked Miss Carrington.

"I'm working at the caramel apple stand," replied Emily Elizabeth. "Later, I'm in the pumpkin-pie-eating contest!"

"What happens to the big pumpkins after the awards are given out?" asked Emily Elizabeth.

Miss Carrington pointed to a poster. "We're making the world's largest pumpkin pie!"

BIG PIE

"The winner of the pie-eating contest will lead the festival parade," said Jetta. "I will be leading the parade."

Jetta and Mac walked away.

"I really want to win," Emily Elizabeth told Clifford.

Emily Elizabeth went to the booth
where Charley and his father, Samuel,
were selling caramel apples.

She had promised to help.

Principal Rodriguez gave out the
award for biggest pumpkin.
He couldn't reach the stem, so
Clifford attached the blue ribbon.

The caramel apple stand was very busy.

Emily Elizabeth handed out caramel apples to customers.

Charley was the cashier.

The apples looked so delicious!

When Samuel made a new batch,

Charley couldn't help eating some.

Almost everyone at the festival wanted a caramel apple.

Emily Elizabeth, Charley, and Samuel worked hard all morning.

In the afternoon, Charley became ill.

"Ow!" he said, looking a little green.

"My stomach hurts."

Emily Elizabeth saw seven caramel

apple cores next to him.

"You ate too many apples," said Samuel.

"Charley, you should go home."

Charley put on his jacket and left.

"Emily Elizabeth," asked Samuel,

"could you stay and help me, please?"

More people got in line,
wanting caramel apples.

Emily Elizabeth stayed and
helped.

Emily Elizabeth sold apples.

It was fun selling people treats.

Emily Elizabeth was glad that she

could help Samuel.

Meanwhile, across the park,
the world's biggest pumpkin pie
was ready to come out of the oven.

Clifford's stomach rumbled.

The pie smelled so good!

While the pie cooled, Clifford visited
Emily Elizabeth at the caramel apple booth.
Emily Elizabeth was still very busy.
"Clifford," she said, "would you please
enter the pie-eating contest in my place?
Samuel needs my help here."

At the pie-eating area, Jetta told
Miss Carrington that Emily Elizabeth
had dropped out of the contest.

"That's too bad," said Miss Carrington.

"I wonder who could take her place?"

Clifford barked.

"Oh, Clifford, it wouldn't be fair for you to enter the contest," said Miss Carrington. "The pies are too small for you."

"I know!" said Miss Carrington. "You can eat the big pie we baked! Perfect! The biggest pumpkin pie for the Big Red Dog."

"On your mark," Miss Carrington
shouted, "get set, and . . . go!"
Everyone gobbled their pies.

Jetta was fast.

T-Bone was faster.

Clifford was the fastest!

Clifford won!

Everyone congratulated Clifford.
Emily Elizabeth ran over to him.
"I'm here!" she said. "The caramel
apple booth ran out of apples."

Clifford barked happily.

All his friends rode on his back

as he led the Harvest Day Festival parade.

What a great prize!

Do You Remember?

Circle the right answer.

1. What was the prize for winning the pie-eating contest?

   a. The world's biggest pumpkin pie

   b. Leading the Harvest Day Festival parade

   c. A tray of caramel apples

2. How did Charley get sick?

   a. He ate too many caramel apples.

   b. He bumped his head.

   c. He ate too much pumpkin pie.

Which happened first?

Which happened next?

Which happened last?

Write a 1, 2, or 3 in the space after each sentence.

The world's biggest pumpkin pie came out of the oven. _____

Clifford won the pie-eating contest. _____

Principal Rodriguez picked the biggest pumpkin contest winner. _____

Answers:

Principal Rodriguez picked the biggest pumpkin contest winner. (1)

Clifford won the pie-eating contest. (3)

The world's biggest pumpkin pie came out of the oven. (2)

2. a

1. b